MRS PORTER

I-SPY

IN THE TOWN

This book belongs to:

WATCH THIS SPACE!

Whenever you go to town, one thing you will notice (no pun intended!) is that there are signs everywhere, pointing things out, telling you what to do, warning you, and so on. Here is a selection.

'Welcome to...' the town you are about to enter.
I-Spy for ***5***
Double for a 'Twinned with...' sign.

Look for unusual street names, especially where the name has changed.
I-Spy for ***25***

Three important facilities you may wish to find: the bus station; railway station (modern sign); and the Tourist Information office.
I-Spy ***5*** *for each*

or ***20*** *for all three on one sign.*

An old British Railways signpost.
I-Spy for ***25***

Six in one, including a sign to the coach park.
*I-Spy **5** for each or **50** for all six on one sign.*

A pedestrian passageway.
*I-Spy for **15***

A pedestrian zone where cars and motorcycles are not permitted but where loading or unloading from a lorry is allowed.
No waiting here either.
*I-Spy for **10***

Another way of indicating a pedestrian zonc. And there is no loading here either between the stated times.
*I-Spy for **10***

And here is the pedestrian precinct itself.
*I-Spy for **10***

The end of the pedestrian area.
*I-Spy for **10***

This flashing orange globe on a black-and-white banded post marks the location of a pedestrian, or zebra, road crossing. Why is it sometimes called a Belisha beacon?

*I-Spy for **5***
Double with answer

And here is the control box for a light-controlled pedestrian crossing, sometimes known as a pelican crossing.
I-Spy for ***5***

Pathway for pedestrians and cyclists only.
I-Spy for ***10***

Direction signs for a cycle route.
I-Spy for ***10***

Cycle access.
I-Spy for ***10***

This sign marks a road closed by a gate to all public traffic except for bicycles.
I-Spy for ***15***

Straight ahead and the left turn are closed by gates to all traffic.
I-Spy for ***15***

The northward direction of a bicycle route but also no traffic heavier than 3 tons may use the road.
I-Spy for ***15***

Riding a bicycle may be a good way of reducing traffic congestion in a town but many traders will not permit bicycles to be leant against their shop window.
I-Spy for ***10***

NO Bicycles against the
window please. Any left
here Will be Removed.

The owners of some buildings make extra efforts to enable easier access for people confined to wheelchairs.
I-Spy for ***15***

Discarded waste is an unsightly problem in many towns and may even be a health hazard. This authority has made a great effort to persuade people to be clean and tidy in this area.
I-Spy for ***15***

Dogs make splendid pets and companions but they can prove troublesome in towns if they are not under proper control. Dogs must be on a lead in this area.
I-Spy for ***10***

Taxis queue here for when you need one.
I-Spy for ***5***

This sign indicates that the lane is for buses only between the hours of 7 am and 7 pm.
*I-Spy for **10***

How to find the town's sports' centre.
*I-Spy for **10***

An unusual hazard perhaps. This sign warns drivers of wildfowl crossing the road...
*I-Spy for **20***

...and this one of a hump-backed bridge.
*I-Spy for **10***

A temporary sign to divert traffic — perhaps because of roadworks along the normal route.
*I-Spy for **10***

To a service area.
*I-Spy for **15***

Sometimes, town parks or other facilities may be closed overnight.
*I-Spy for **10***

Few towns now have their own prisons or gaols. This sign marks the site where a prison once stood.
*I-Spy for **15***

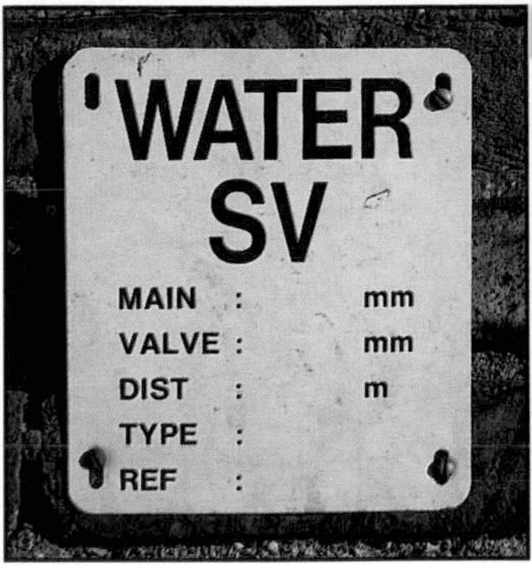

...and this is a stop valve or shut-off valve.
*I-Spy for **10***

You might see signs like this one on a wall. It indicates the position of a valve that can control the water supply for a large area...
*I-Spy for **10***

Where there is high-voltage electricity, you may see a warning sign like this one. It certainly makes its point clear!
*I-Spy for **10***

As towns grow busier and there are more vehicles on the road, local authorities continue to have to find ways of coping with all the vehicles that people wish to park so that they can go shopping or use some other town service.

Sometimes it is easier to travel by bicycle in a town. But you may still have to leave a cycle somewhere. Here is a modern sign pointing to a bicycle park...
I-Spy for ***5***

...and an old one.
I-Spy for ***10***

Here is the cycle parking on street-level racks. Notice that most of the bicycles are chained for security.
I-Spy for ***5***

Motorcycles also have their own special parking areas. How to get there...
I-Spy for ***5***

...and the motorcycle parking.
I-Spy for ***5***
Double if it is for 'solo motor cycles only'.

This sign points to a long-stay car park where there are also toilets with facilities for disabled people, as well as a bottle bank.
I-Spy for ***5***

There is often a charge for parking a car. In this car park, you must buy a ticket and display it in the car at all times between 8.00 am and 6.30 pm, Monday to Saturday. At other times, the parking may be free.
I-Spy for ***5***

There may be a barrier to prevent vehicles over a certain height from entering the park.
I-Spy for ***10***

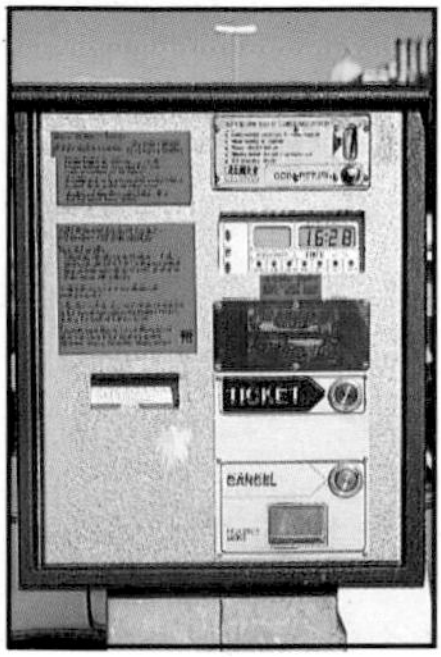

Here is the machine where drivers may purchase their 'pay and display' tickets before leaving the car in the park.
*I-Spy for **5***

Sometimes parking may be allowed at the kerbside. This may be for a limited period except on Sundays.
*I-Spy for **5***

Disabled drivers may be provided with their own special parking areas where other drivers should not park their cars.
*I-Spy for **10***

Doctors, too, may have their own parking areas provided they have the correct permit.
*I-Spy for **10***

In some towns and cities, parking may be permitted along the streets. The roadsides are marked out into car parking spaces, and there is a meter for each space. The driver inserts coins into the meter to set it. The meter shows how much time the driver has bought. Sometimes, though, neither parking nor loading is allowed, and the meters are covered with special hoods.
*I-Spy for **15***

This sign shows that there is 'no waiting' between the times specified...
I-Spy for ***10***

... and 'No loading' between the designated times.
I-Spy for ***10***

These plastic 'no waiting' cones may be positioned by the police if they need to prevent parking or loading in an area where it may normally be allowed...
I-Spy for ***10***

Traffic Wardens are common in towns to ensure that the parking regulations are enforced. They are entitled to issue tickets to drivers parking illegally.
I-Spy for ***5***

This notice has been designed to deter drivers from parking on a privately owned space.
I-Spy for ***15***

The pedestrian precincts in some towns may have entertainment for children. Here is a roundabout for younger children.
*I-Spy for **10***

Balloons on legs or a half-hidden street vendor?
*I-Spy for **10***

Barrel organs were once a common form of street entertainment. Nowadays, they are seen less often although they may be making a comeback, mainly for entertainment value.
*I-Spy for **20***

This street entertainer is playing an accordion. What name is usually given to street musicians?
*I-Spy for **10** — double with answer* ____________________

You don't have to go into a café or even a fast food shop to satisfy your hunger. Sometimes, there are fast food stalls on the street.
I-Spy for ***10***

A pavement stall where cut flowers are sold.
I-Spy for ***5***

Many towns still have their market squares and street markets. Some of these markets have been held regularly for hundreds of years.
I-Spy for ***5***

In this case, an auctioneer is trying to get the best price for lots brought along for sale by local people.
I-Spy for ***20***

A lottery is a way of raising money by selling numbered tickets. Some of these tickets are drawn randomly later and the holder of the ticket wins a prize.
I-Spy for ***10***

A town crier is a person employed by the town to make public proclamations. Traditionally, before he reads the proclamation, the crier shouts 'Oyez!' three times. This means 'Hear!' or 'Attend!'.
I-Spy for ***25***

A girl delivering the morning papers. To make her work easier, she has a trolley, and the dog is there for company.
I-Spy for ***10***

How do they water all those plants, high up on buildings or in hanging baskets on lamp posts? Now you can see.
*I-Spy for **15***

Reroofing using slate, a traditional roofing material, to fit in with the local architecture.
*I-Spy for **10***

Painting the front. The whole of the facade of a building housing a Tandoori Restaurant is being repainted. What does tandoori mean?

____

*I-Spy for **10** — double with answer*

When high buildings have to be painted or repaired, scaffolding is erected first.
*I-Spy for **10***

Many shops and offices are fitted with alarms which will sound if a burglar tries to break into the building. The windows and doors may be wired. There may be pressure pads under carpets which will set off the alarm if someone walks over them. There may even be infra-red beams that sound the alarm if they are broken. The company that fitted the alarm system is usually named on the outside of the box that houses the bell or siren. And this box is usually placed in a prominent position to warn that the building has an alarm system.

*I-Spy **5** each for five different alarm companies.*

LIGHTING THE WAY

London streets were first lit by gas lighting in 1807, and, early in the twentieth century, electric street lighting was being installed throughout Britain and Europe. There is a variety of types of street lighting, many of which are designed to complement the local architecture. Some lights have a bulb with an incandescent filament, similar to home lighting. Others produce light by passing an electric current through a metal vapour. Sodium is commonly used for this because it produces a good yellow light with little glare. What other metal has been used for street lights, and what colour light does it produce?

*I-Spy **5** each for ten different styles of street lighting. Double with answers.*

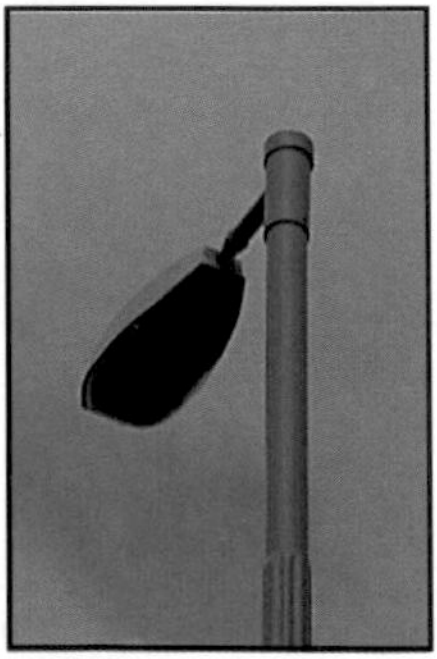

7

Public services, such as water, gas, electricity, or telephone, are often carried beneath the streets. The companies need to have access to parts of the networks so, if you look carefully, you will see many different kinds of gratings and manhole covers that have been used, over many years, by different companies and services. Here are some examples...

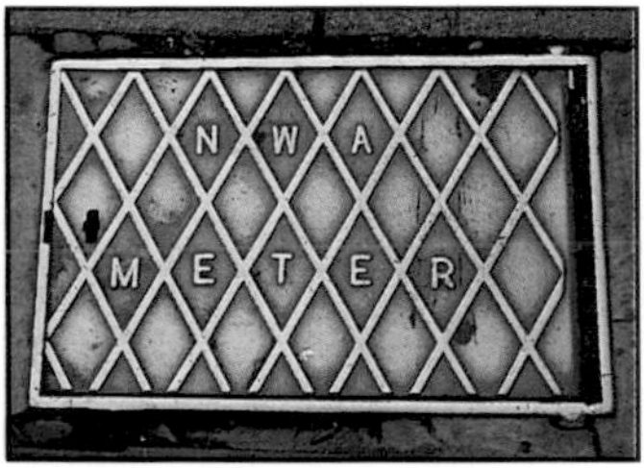

... access to a water authority meter

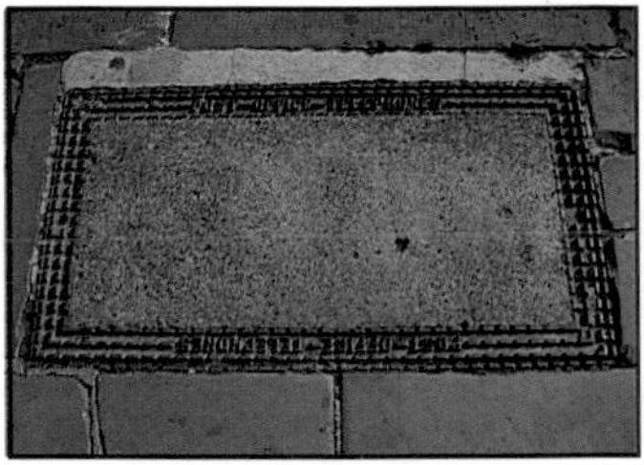

...a cover to telephone cables when these were operated by the Post Office

...gas

...an unusual type of cover

*I-Spy **5** for each of water, gas, electricity, and telephone.*

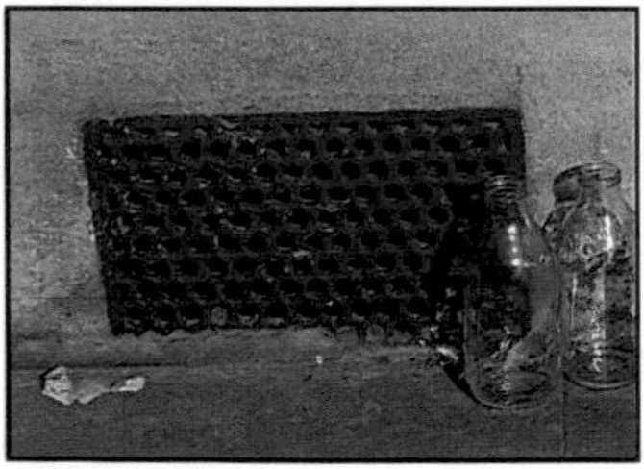

And here is an iron grill that allows air to flow beneath the floor of a building to stop it becoming damp.
*I-Spy for **10***

One reason why many people have to come into town is to visit a bank. They may wish to pay money into a bank account, withdraw money, or carry out some other transaction such as paying bills or arranging for some foreign currency.

Barclays
I-Spy for ***5***

Clydesdale
I-Spy for ***5***

Lloyds
I-Spy for ***5***

National Westminster
I-Spy for ***5***

Midland
I-Spy for ***5***

TSB
I-Spy for ***5***

Some bank transactions, such as withdrawing cash or requesting a balance, can be carried out through machines set in the wall.
I-Spy ***5*** *for any two.*

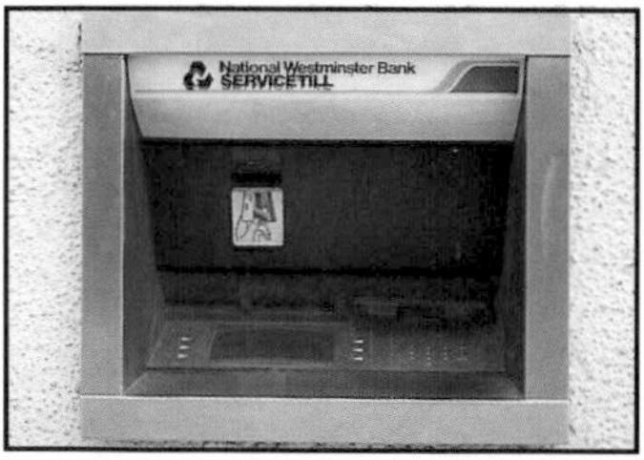

The Royal Bank of Scotland
I-Spy for ***5***

Yorkshire Bank
I-Spy for ***10***

On buildings, such as service stations or where there is a room with electrical equipment, there may be a fireman's switch set high up on an outside wall. This enables the fire officer to switch off the electricity supply.
*I-Spy **10** for each of two different kinds.*

Buildings, such as hotels or offices, may have separate exits in case of fire. This sign warns everyone not to obstruct such an exit.
*I-Spy for **10***

Every sizeable town has its fire station. Here a fire appliance is just pulling out — perhaps to speed off to an emergency.
*I-Spy for **10***

Here is a bus garage. When not in use, the buses are housed in a garage such as this.
*I-Spy for **15***

Many towns have a central bus station although some are now used for other purposes.
*I-Spy for **10***

You'll often find a bus timetable at a bus stop explaining the services that operate on that route.
*I-Spy for **5***

Bus stop. This one has an elaborate iron-work shelter.
*I-Spy for **10***

Traders, retailers, or other facilities may be advertised with appropriate signs. Before people could read, traders relied on picture signs to tell customers what they did or sold.

A bicycle shop
*I-Spy for **5** for the shop*
Double if it has an unusual sign

A pharmacy. The mortar and pestle above the green cross indicate the trade, too.
*I-Spy for **5** for the shop*
Double if it has an unusual sign

A barber's shop. The red and white suggest red blood on white bandages from the days when barbers were also surgeons.
*I-Spy for **5** for the shop — double if it has an unusual sign*

A sports shop.
*I-Spy for **5** for the shop — double if it has an unusual sign*

A painting of a blacksmith's anvil tells instantly what this trader does.
*I-Spy for **5** for the shop — double if it has an unusual sign*

Look out for spinners outside shop doorways. This shop specializes in souvenirs of Oxford.
*I-Spy for **5***

It is not only the AA patrols on a car journey that you can I-Spy. Here is an AA insurance office in the town.
*I-Spy for **10***

Coal merchant. Not quite such a common sight in towns nowadays since more people have turned to gas and electricity for their basic heating needs.
*I-Spy for **10** for the shop*
Double if it has an unusual sign

A smart market arcade.
*I-Spy for **10***

The very first fast food, perhaps, a traditional fish and chip shop.
*I-Spy for **5***

A stationer's shop where I-Spy is in!
*I-Spy for **5***

Public houses often have elaborate inn signs but here is an unusual one that incorporates a clock as well as an animal. What is a white hart?

*I-Spy for **10** — double with answer*

It is not only pubs that have their signs; clubs do, too. Here are three different clubs.

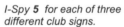

*I-Spy **5** for each of three different club signs.*

Most resort towns once had their ballrooms where residents and visitors went to enjoy a waltz or a foxtrot. Now they are not so common. Here is an elegant sign with its decorative ironwork.
*I-Spy for **20***

Every sizeable town has its Post Office. Here is solid-looking building in stone and slate.
I-Spy for ***10***

The well-known traditional red pillar box. Interestingly, the oblong box on the side is to contain extra pouches for times when the collecting postal worker is overloaded.
I-Spy for ***5***
Double for one with the pouch box

You have to turn up at the right time to Spy a postal worker emptying the Post Office mail boxes.
I-Spy for ***15***

Not quite so common, a large double pillar box. Why is it marked with a crown and the letters 'GR'?

___

___

*I-Spy for **10** — double with answer*

And a post box set in the wall together with a machine dispensing books of stamps.
*I-Spy for **10***

Finally, a modern coin-operated stamp machine.
*I-Spy for **10***

Towns often honour famous men and women who have lived or died there by erecting a plaque or stone to mark the spot.

The martyrdom of Latimer, Ridley, and Cranmer, leaders of the Protestant Reformation, who were burnt as heretics.

John Hampden who defended the rights of the House of Commons against King Charles I.

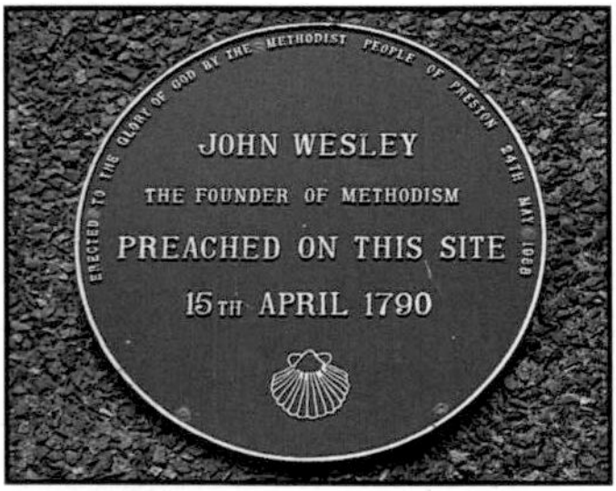

The Methodist preacher, John Wesley.

☐ ☐ ☐ ☐

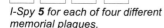

*I-Spy **5** for each of four different memorial plaques.*

In honour of King George V.

More and more towns are offering facilities for the collection of materials for recycling. Bottle banks, can banks, and bins, like this one, for collecting old newspapers are the most common.

I-Spy ***10*** *for each of three.*

Less usual, here, The Spastics Society has set up a collection point for second-hand clothes and other good-quality materials.
I-Spy for ***20***

Here is a 'Postman Pat' collecting box in aid of the National Society for the Prevention of Cruelty to Children.
I-Spy ***10*** *each for any two different boxes like this.*

And to entertain the youngsters while Mum or Dad is shopping, a coin-operated ride outside a shop.
I-Spy for ***5***

A coin-operated 'parrot-in-a-cage' picks up the bubble gum and sends it down the chute.
*I-Spy for **10***

And to keep your town tidy, the local authority places litter bins to take your rubbish. Here are three including a 'wheelie bin'.
*I-Spy **5** for each of three different kinds.*

For those on the town's outskirts, in the country, or for people who are unable to get into the town centre easily, many local authorities run a valuable mobile library service.
I-Spy for ***10***

Another welcome facility is the local allotments. For a modest fee, local people may rent a small plot of land on which to grow vegetables.
I-Spy for ***10***

The beautifully kept grass of a bowling green.
I-Spy for ***10***

A canal and towpath, once used for transporting goods, now offers anglers relaxing recreation.
*I-Spy for **10***

Few towns have full-size race-courses for horse racing. Those that do are often famous.
*I-Spy for **20***

And if you are tired from all that recreation or from shopping, towns usually offer benches to rest on. A straightforward wooden one...
*I-Spy for **5***

...or a more modern wood and ironwork bench.
*I-Spy for **5***

An important facility in any town is its public lavatories. Here the approach to the women's toilet beneath street level has been made more attractive by decorative ironwork...
*I-Spy for **10***

...and a thoughtful local authority has made special arrangements for the disabled, even including an alarm system.
*I-Spy for **15***

The cemetery is the town's main burial ground not attached to a church. A well-kept cemetery is a peaceful place and is often a haven for wildlife in an urban setting.
*I-Spy for **10***

Many towns have a drinking fountain, but few are as elaborate as this one. Apparently, the sculptor forgot to give the ram any ears!
*I-Spy for **15***

Milestones can still be seen by the sides of roads, They date from the time when the toll roads were introduced. But, here, on the wall of the town hall is a plate showing the distances of other important towns and cities.
*I-Spy for **10***

This machine enables consumers with budget meters for their electricity supply to pay using pound coins to enable them to recharge their keys.
*I-Spy for **15***

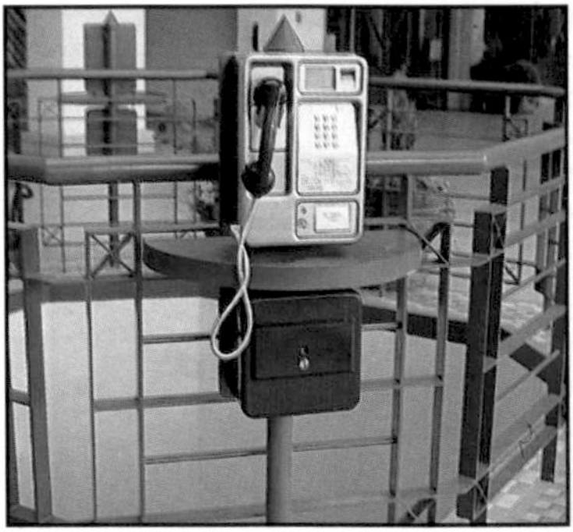

A new British Telecom coin-operated public telephone inside a smart arcade.
*I-Spy for **10***

Have you ever wondered what these green cabinets are? You might see one open with a British Telecom engineer working with wires and cables. The cabinet gives access to the point where the main telephone line in an area splits into the smaller lines to go to each place where there is a phone.
*I-Spy for **10***

Mini-roundabouts can be seen in most towns. The same rules apply to traffic as for a large roundabout.
I-Spy for ***5***

Before tarmac and concrete were available, town streets were sometimes cobbled, like this one. The cobbles are rounded stones or setts. Cobbled streets are not very common nowadays.
I-Spy for ***20***

Some shops may decorated their frontages with elaborate mosaic patterns...
I-Spy for ***15***

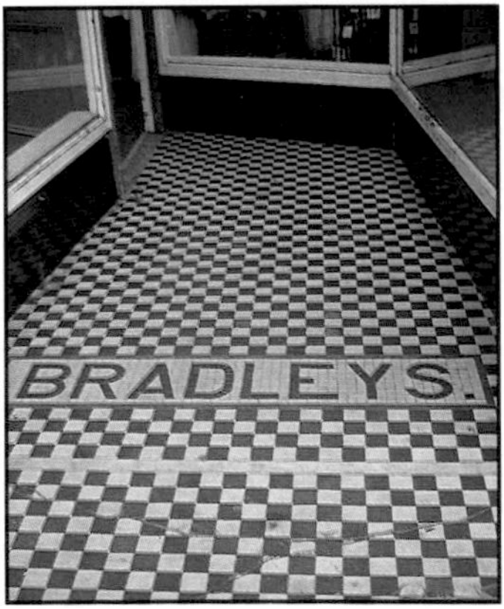

...or the floors may be intricately tiled, even including the name of the business.
I-Spy for ***10***

Elegant iron railings topped with a proud lion mark the front boundary of this town house.
*I-Spy for **10***

A graceful pair of iron pillars holds a local information board.
*I-Spy for **10***

Iron bollards bar the way to all traffic but pedestrians and bicycles...
*I-Spy for **10***

... and a gate does, too.
*I-Spy for **10***

Major shops or banks will sometimes offer passers-by the time by way of elaborate ironwork clocks.
I-Spy for ***10***

And, perched on a tall mast a weather cock points out the direction of the wind.
I-Spy for ***10***

The balconies of some smart town houses may be adorned with painted wrought iron.
I-Spy for ***10***

Or shops may protect their window-shopping customers with an ironwork veranda.
I-Spy for ***10***

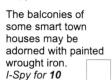

Medieval towns often grew up around castles. In times of war, the townspeople could quickly be taken into the castle for protection.
*I-Spy for **20***

Every town has its town hall or municipal building although they are not always as grand as these magnificent offices.
*I-Spy for **10***

Sometimes, large companies, such as financial institutions or shipping lines, were able to build very grand headquarters.
*I-Spy for **15***

The Public Library often houses a reading room, a collection of music recordings, journals, newspapers, and even 'talking books' as well as its books. This one has an elegant Georgian-style frontage.
I-Spy for ***10***

This 'Everyman' theatre is typical of many town theatres built during the nineteenth century.
I-Spy for ***10***

Most larger towns or cities run their own local newspapers. Here is the office of the *Echo* and the *Chronicle*.
I-Spy for ***10***

A Regency-style frontage conceals an ultra-modern shopping arcade.
I-Spy for ***15***

And this large but austere-looking brick building houses a modern cinema.
I-Spy for ***10***

When it is not being used for its original purpose, the area enclosed by a covered market is often used for extra car parking. Notice the ornate wrought ironwork.
I-Spy for ***10***

This double-fronted slate and sandstone building houses the town's police station.
*I-Spy for **10***

Modern Tourist Information Offices are often housed in buildings that once had another purpose.
*I-Spy for **10***

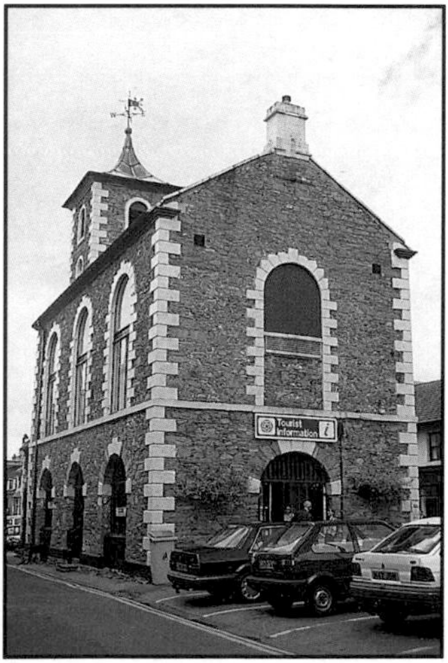

Where the local water company needs to keep up the water pressure for supply to the town's customers, they are often obliged to build a water tower. This one looks more like a watch tower, though.
*I-Spy for **10***

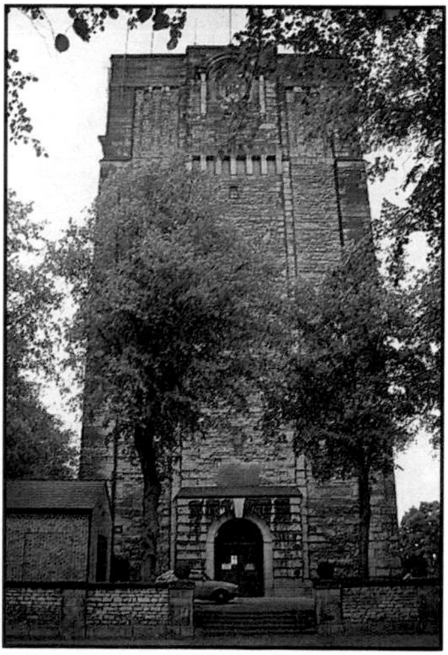

Cities, rather than towns, have cathedrals. They are usually magnificently imposing buildings that may have taken scores of years to build...
*I-Spy for **10***

... but every town has at least one church...
*I-Spy for **5***

... where a wedding service may be held.
*I-Spy for **10***

The parish church may have a community hall attached or nearby. This one is being used as a reading room and for the sale of books.
*I-Spy for **10***

A typical, stone-built Victorian primary school still in use today.
*I-Spy for **10***

Old industrial buildings, such as this large, nineteenth-century flour mill may take on a new lease of life as housing when its working days are over.
*I-Spy for **15***

Answers
Belisha beacon: named after Leslie Hore Belisha, British Minister of Transport from 1934-37.
Street musician: busker.
Painting the front: a tandoor is a flask-shaped clay oven used to cook tandoori-style Indian food.
Lighting the way: mercury, bluish green light.
Inn sign: a white hart is a male red deer with a white coat.
Double pillar box: the crown is for the Royal Mail and GR stands for George Rex, the king on the throne when the pillar box was installed.

ISBN (paperback) 1 85671 107 2

Michelin Tyre Public Limited Company
Davy House, Lyon Road, Harrow, Middlesex HA1 2DQ

A CIP record for this title is available from the British Library.

Edited and designed by Curtis Garratt Limited, The Old Vicarage, Horton cum Studley, Oxford OX9 1BT

The Publisher gratefully acknowledges the contribution of Richard Garratt who provided all of the photographs in this I-Spy book.

Colour reproduction by Norwich Litho Services Limited.

Printed in Spain.